English
made easy

Key Stage 2
ages 10-11

Author
John Hesk

LONDON • NEW YORK • MUNICH • MELBOURNE • DELHI

Homophones and homographs

Some words sound the same as other words. Choose words that sound the same to fill in the gaps in each sentence below. D
Remember: A **homophone** is a word that sounds the same as another word but has a different meaning and is sometimes spelt differently.
For example: I don't know **where** you are going to **wear** that hat!

Ben asked if he could come t__ the match t__ __,
but we only have t__ __ tickets.

They're fetching t__ __ __ __ jackets from the cloakroom over t__ __ __ __.

W__ __'__ the owner of this coat – I can't tell w__ __ __ __ is w__ __ __ __?

We can't tell w__ __ __ __ __ __ the __ __ __ __ __ __ __ __ will be dry or wet.

Underline the **homographs** in the sentence below.
Remember: A **homograph** is a word that has the same spelling as another word but has a different meaning.

I went to a football match one cold Saturday. I wore a striped scarf and hat to match. Afterwards, I watched while Mum put a match to the fire.

In the following sentences, the **homographs** are underlined. Read each sentence, and then write another sentence that changes the meaning of the **homograph**.

The old castle had a huge, square <u>keep</u>.

....

I am planning an expedition to the South <u>Pole</u>.

....

Our dog likes me to throw a <u>stick</u>.

....

She won a new computer in the prize <u>draw</u>.

....

He <u>ground</u> the maize to make flour.

....

Puns

Complete this list of **homophones** by writing another word that sounds the same but has a different spelling. D

aloud   *allowed* ....   board   ....

buoy   ....   canon   ....

cereal   ....   chord   ....

course   ....   draught   ....

hair   ....   hoarse   ....

leak   ....   lessen   ....

moor   ....   pale   ....

pause   ....   plane   ....

right   ....   sew   ....

stair   ....   tale   ....

waist   ....   new   ....

pair   ....   bear   ....

Now choose some of the paired words to write **punning** sentences.
Remember: Puns are jokes that rely on **homophones** for their humour.
For example: My pony is a little hoarse today.

....

....

....

....

....

....

Riddles

Can you solve this word-building **riddle**?

My first is in **bread** but not in **bead**.
My second is in **dig** but not in **dug**.
My third is in **fled** but not in **flew**.
My fourth is in **hid** but not in **hit**.
My fifth is in **held** but not in **herd**.
My sixth is in **step** but not in **stop**.

Answer ....

Now try this one.

My first is in **bite** but not in **site**.
My second is in **tent** but not in **tint**.
My third is in **grow** but not in **brow**.
My fourth is in **in** but not in **on**.
My fifth is in **ton** but not in **tow**.
My sixth is in **stone** but not in **store**.
My seventh is in **pin** but not in **pun**.
My eighth is in **naught** but not in **caught**.
My ninth is in **grip** but not in **drip**.

Answer ....

Try to make some word-building **riddles** of your own. Choose from the list of words below.
The first one has been started for you. Continue your **riddles** on an extra sheet of paper.

business	colonel	family	friend	height	necessary
immediate	medicine	neighbour	occasion	queue	rhythm
separate	skilful	twelfth	weird	yacht	

My first is in **bite** but not in **mite**.
My second is in **cup** but not in **cap**.
My third is in **sew** but not in **dew**.
My fourth is in **in** but not in **an**.
My fifth is in **ton** but not in **toe**.

My sixth is in .... but not in ....

My seventh is in .... but not in ....

My eighth is in .... but not in ....

Opposites

Read this **poem** aloud.

Some Opposites

What is the opposite of *riot*?
It's *lots of people keeping quiet.*

The opposite of *doughnut*? Wait
A minute while I meditate.
This isn't easy. Ah, I've found it!
A cookie with a hole around it.

What is the opposite of *two*?
A lonely me, a lonely you.

The opposite of a cloud could be
A white reflection in the sea,
Or a huge blueness in the air,
Caused by a cloud's not being there.

The opposite of *opposite*?
That's much too difficult. I quit.

Richard Wilbur

In the list below, underline the words that can have **opposites**, and draw a ring around those that cannot. Then write down the underlined words and their **opposites**.

| far | door | blue | wrong | grass | quickly | pencil | light |
| happy | fridge | ten | town | small | computer | duck | |

far - near,
....

....

Now look at the words you have ringed. Pick three, and make up **words** or **phrases** that could be "joke" **opposites** for them. Write your "joke" **opposites** and your reasons below.

door - wall (a wall is what is left if you have no door!)
....

....

....

....

You may have found words that cannot even have "joke" **opposites**. Write them here.

....

Spoonerisms

Kinquering congs is a well-known example of a **spoonerism**. W. A. Spooner from Oxford, England, accidentally "invented" **spoonerisms**: he often mixed up the sounds at the beginning of his words.

What did W. A. Spooner mean to say instead of kinquering congs?

....

Here are some modern **spoonerisms** for you to "translate" into English – take care with the spelling! D

Did you hear the roar-bell ding?

....

Don't forget to dock the law!

....

We had thick frog last fiday.

....

Do you like to bead in red?

....

I can fee my sootprints!

....

I caught a ban of lemon drink.

....

Can you think of any **spoonerisms** yourself? Write them here.

....

....

....

Malapropisms

Mrs. Malaprop is a character in a play by R. B. Sheridan. She often gets her words mixed up, using a word that sounds almost, but not quite, like the correct one. For instance, she says the word **allegory** when she means to say **alligator**!

Look up the word **allegory** in the dictionary, then explain the obvious difference between **allegory** and **alligator**. ⬚D

....

....

....

Here are some **malapropisms** for you to correct – draw a ring around the word that is used incorrectly, then rewrite the sentence using the correct word. ⬚D

There are three angels in a triangle.

....

We decided to sign the partition.

....

I am pleased to except this prize.

....

The brakes on a bike work by fraction.

....

The jugular prepared to pounce.

....

Now find the meanings of the words you ringed, and write them here. ⬚D

....

....

....

....

....

Inventing words

Use a **dictionary** to complete these **definitions**. ☐D

A micro *chip* is a very small chip of silicone.

A microprocessor is a ....

A .... is the climate of a very small area.

A .... is a very small living thing.

An instrument used to look at very small objects is a ....

Find three more words beginning with the **prefix** micro- and explain their.meanings. ☐D

A micro .... is ....

A micro .... is ....

A micro .... is ....

Now make up some new "micro" words, and **define** them. For example, a microsnack is a snack that is too small to be satisfying but too tasty to resist.

....

....

....

Complete these **definitions**. ☐D

A mega *byte* is a very large unit of computer memory.

A megaphone is a ....

A megamouth is a shark with a ....

A megalopolis is a ....

A .... is a very large stone or rock.

Now make up some "mega" words, and **define** them. For example, a megamouse is an extra-large mouse from the planet Megary.

....

....

....

Similes

Some **similes**, such as "like a house on fire", are called **cliches** because they are so overused that they have very little impact. It is a good idea to use new **similes** in your writing, as they attract interest and help your reader to imagine what you are describing. **Remember**: A **simile** is something compared with something else to create an image in the reader's mind. It usually includes the words **like** or **as**.

Practise writing new **similes** by thinking of original comparisons for these **adjectives**.

as light as *a petal* ....

as good as ....

as dull as ....

as clean as ....

as quick as ....

as dry as ....

as heavy as ....

as pretty as ....

as big as ....

as rich as ....

Complete these sentences by thinking of **similes** for the **verbs**.

He crawled like *a snail* ....

The athlete ran like ....

The small boat sank like ....

It rained like ....

Complete these sentences by thinking of **similes** for the **nouns**.

The heat was like *a blazing bonfire* ....

The thick mud felt as if ....

The black smoke smelt like ....

The music she played sounded like ....

The fresh water tasted like ....

The overgrown garden looked as if ....

Metaphors

Read this **poem** aloud.

What is the Sun?

the Sun is an orange dinghy
    sailing across a calm sea

it is a gold coin
    dropped down a drain in Heaven

the Sun is a yellow beach ball
    kicked high into the summer sky

it is a red thumb-print
    on a sheet of pale blue paper

the Sun is a milk bottle's gold top
    floating in a puddle

Wes Magee

How many **metaphors** for the Sun can you find in this **poem**? Make a list of them below.
Remember: A **metaphor** is something described as if it were something else. It is like
a simile but does not include the words like or as.

an orange dinghy.

....

....

Rewrite one of the five **verses**, and change the **metaphor** to a **simile**. To do this, you
only need to add one word.

....

....

....

Pick a **verse** from the **poem**, and write a short paragraph explaining what is meant by
the description of the Sun.

....

....

Which of the **metaphors** in the **poem** seems most effective to you? Why?

....

....

Write your own metaphors

Use the pattern of the **poem** on page 10 to write a **poem** of your own that includes **metaphors**. Choose one of the **titles** below or make up your own.

What is a cloud?

What is the sea?

What is the Moon?

What is ....? (your choice)

.... (title)

....

....

....

....

....

....

....

....

....

Sentence-building

Simple sentences can be made longer by adding **clauses**. A **compound sentence** consists of two or more clauses of equal importance. A **complex sentence** consists of one or more main clauses and another clause that needs the others to make complete sense.

Jack heard a strange noise. (**simple sentence** – one clause)

Jack heard a strange noise, and we were scared. (**compound sentence** – two simple sentences joined by **and** to make two equally important clauses)

Jack heard a strange noise, and we were scared when he told us about it. (**complex sentence** – there is a third clause, which needs the others to make complete sense.)

Build these **simple sentences** into **compound sentences** by adding a clause of equal importance. The first one has been done for you.
Remember: A **clause** is a group of words that includes a verb.

The dog barked.

The dog barked but we didn't hear anything.

The rain fell.

....

She ran across the park.

....

The computer crashed.

....

Now build your **compound sentences** into **complex sentences** by adding another clause.

The dog barked, but we didn't hear anything because the television was too loud.

....

....

....

....

Different types of writing

The text extracts below could have come from any of the following types of writing: **instructions, explanations, poems, folk tales, novels, information** or **arguments**. Read each extract, then decide which type of writing it is.

Stop! Before you throw anything away, think … ....

The old miller knew he had not long to live so … ....

If the water is added gradually to the powder in the test tube, then … ....

Thus, the water evaporates and returns to the atmosphere. ....

That peculiar person from Putney! ....

The day was warm, though cloudy, and I noticed a strange scent in the air … ....

a blue-grey day a Saturday ....

Surely you must realise that … ....

Add the beaten egg … ....

The second planet from the Sun is called … ....

Choose one of the above extracts that comes from a **fiction** book. Imagine what the rest of the paragraph might look like, and write a draft version on a separate sheet of paper. Then write the finished paragraph below.
Remember: Fiction means text that was invented by the writer.

....

....

....

....

If you want to, do the same thing by choosing an extract from a **non-fiction** book. Write the paragraph on a separate sheet of paper.
Remember: Non-fiction means that the information in the piece of writing is factual.

Comparing poems

Read these two **poems** aloud, listening to the **rhythms** and the **sounds**.

1
I Am the Rain

I am the rain
I like to play games
like sometimes
    I pretend
I'm going
    to fall
Man that's the time
I don't come at all
Like sometimes
I get these laughing stitches
up my sides
    rushing people in
and out
    with the clothesline
I just love drip
    dropping
down collars
    and spines
Maybe it's a shame
but it's the only way
I get some fame

Grace Nichols

2
Sky

Tall and blue
true and open

So open my arms have room
for all the world
for sun and moon
    for birds and stars

Yet how I wish I had the chance
to come drifting down to earth –
    a simple bed sheet
covering some little girl or boy
just for a night
    but I am Sky
    that's why

Grace Nichols

Can you find some pairs of **half-rhymes** in these poems? List them below.
Remember: Half-rhymes are words that nearly rhyme. For example: pan/pun, wreck/rack.

Poem 1 ....

Poem 2 ....

Read the **poems** again, listening to the **beat** and the **rhythm**. Are they the same in both poems?

....

Can you find any repeated **vowel sounds** in the **poems**? If so, write them below.
Remember: The letters **a**, **e**, **i**, **o** and **u** are **vowels**. The letter **y** is sometimes also a **vowel**.

Poem 1 ....

Poem 2 ....

Investigating poems

Reread the **poems** on page 14. What do you notice about the **punctuation** in both poems?

....

....

What do you notice about the way the poems are **set out**? Look where the lines start.

....

....

Who or what is speaking in poem 1?

....

Who or what is speaking in poem 2?

....

Can these poems be placed under the same heading? If so, what might that heading be?

....

What evidence is there that *Sky* and *I Am the Rain* were written by the same **poet**? Answer this question by writing a **paragraph**; use some of your answers to the questions above, and any other similarities you may have noticed.

....

....

....

....

....

....

....

....

....

Fast fact-finding

Read the passage below.

 **Sky Colours**

HAVE YOU EVER WONDERED why clear skies are sometimes deep blue and at other times almost white? Or why some sunsets are fiery red and others watery yellow? The reason is that the mixture of particles in the atmosphere is constantly changing. Every colour in the sky comes from the Sun. Sunlight is white, which means it is a mix of every colour in the rainbow. But as it passes through the atmosphere, gases, dust, ice crystals and water droplets split it into the various colours, bouncing some towards our eyes and absorbing others. The colours we see depend on which colours are reflected and which are absorbed. Clear skies are blue because gases in the air reflect mostly blue light from the Sun. The sky gets paler when extra dust or moisture reflects other colours, diluting the blue. Sunsets are yellow (or red, if the air is dusty) because the Sun's rays have to travel so far through the lower atmosphere that all the yellow light is absorbed.

From *How the Earth Works* by John Farndon

Underline all the **main points** in the paragraph above. Then answer these questions in full sentences.

What colour is sunlight?

....

Why is the sky blue?

....

....

What do you notice about the first four words? Why do you think they are set out this way?

....

....

What kind of sentences introduce the passage?

....

....

Words such as **the reason is**, **because** and **which means** tell us that this piece of writing does more than simply list facts. What else does it do?

....

....

Answer Section with Parents' Notes

Key Stage 2
Ages 10–11

This 8-page section provides answers or explanatory notes to all the activities in this book. This will enable you to assess your child's work.

Point out any spelling mistakes, incorrect punctuation and grammatical errors as you mark each page. Also correct any handwriting errors. (Your child should use the handwriting style taught at his or her school.) As well as making corrections, it is very important to praise your child's efforts and achievements.

Encourage your child to use a dictionary, and suggest that he or she uses a notebook to compile a **word bank** of new words or difficult spellings.

---

2 ⭐ ## Homophones and homographs

Some words sound the same as other words. Choose words that sound the same to fill in the gaps in each sentence below. D
Remember: A **homophone** is a word that sounds the same as another word but has a different meaning and is sometimes spelt differently.
For example: I don't know **where** you are going to **wear** that hat!

Ben asked if he could come t o the match t o o, but we only have t w o tickets.

They're fetching t h e i r jackets from the cloakroom over t h e r e.

W h o's the owner of this coat – I can't tell w h o s e is w h o s e?

We can't tell w h e t h e r the w e a t h e r will be dry or wet.

Underline the **homographs** in the sentence below.
Remember: A **homograph** is a word that has the same spelling as another word but has a different meaning.

I went to a football <u>match</u> one cold Saturday. I wore a striped scarf and hat to <u>match</u>. Afterwards, I watched while Mum put a <u>match</u> to the fire.

In the following sentences, the **homographs** are underlined. Read each sentence, and then write another sentence that changes the meaning of the **homograph**.

The old castle had a huge, square <u>keep</u>.

....

I am planning an expedition to the South <u>Pole</u>.

....

Our dog likes me to throw a <u>stick</u>.

....

She won a new computer in the raffle <u>draw</u>.

....

He <u>ground</u> the maize to make flour.

Answers may vary

On this page your child practises using some common homophones and homographs. Children often find these words confusing, so you may need to offer help with these exercises. Remember to praise your child's correct answers.

---

3 ## Puns ⭐

Complete this list of **homophones** by writing another word that sounds the same but has a different spelling. D

aloud	*allowed*	board	*bored*
buoy	*boy*	canon	*cannon*
cereal	*serial*	chord	*cord*
course	*coarse*	draught	*draft*
hair	*hare*	hoarse	*horse*
leak	*leek*	lessen	*lesson*
moor	*more*	pale	*pail*
pause	*paws*	plane	*plain*
right	*write*	sew	*so*
stair	*stare*	tale	*tail*
waist	*waste*	new	*knew*
pair	*pear*	bear	*bare*

Now choose some of the paired words to write **punning** sentences.
Remember: Puns are jokes that rely on **homophones** for their humour.
For example: My pony is a little hoarse today.

....
....
....
....
....
....

Answers may vary

The exercises on this page provide further practice with homophones. Check that your child writes his or her puns in complete sentences and selects the correct homophone for each context. Encourage him or her to have fun with this activity.

---

4 ⭐ ## Riddles

Can you solve this word-building **riddle**?

My first is in **bread** but not in **bead**.
My second is in **dig** but not in **dug**.
My third is in **fled** but not in **flew**.
My fourth is in **hid** but not in **hit**.
My fifth is in **held** but not in **herd**.
My sixth is in **step** but not in **stop**.

Answer _riddle_

Now try this one.

My first is in **bite** but not in **site**.
My second is in **tent** but not in **tint**.
My third is in **grow** but not in **brow**.
My fourth is in **in** but not in **on**.
My fifth is in **ton** but not in **tow**.
My sixth is in **stone** but not in **store**.
My seventh is in **pin** but not in **pun**.
My eighth is in **naught** but not in **caught**.
My ninth is in **grip** but not in **drip**.

Answer _beginning_

Try to make some word-building **riddles** of your own. Choose from the list of words below. The first one has been started for you. Continue your **riddles** on an extra sheet of paper.

business	colonel	family	friend	height	necessary
immediate	medicine	neighbour	occasion	queue	rhythm
separate	skilful	twelfth	weird	yacht	

My first is in **bite** but not in **mite**.
My second is in **cup** but not in **cap**.
My third is in **sew** but not in **dew**.
My fourth is in **in** but not in **an**.
My fifth is in **ton** but not in **toe**.

My sixth is in .... but not in ....

My seventh is in .... but not in ....

My eighth is in .... but not in ....

Answers may vary

These activities, based on riddles, help draw your child's attention to the spelling of some common words that are often misspelt. The formula for these riddles can be reversed if it helps. For example: My first is in *first* and also in *fourth*.

Opposites

Read this **poem** aloud.

Some Opposites

What is the opposite of *riot*?
It's *lots of people keeping quiet.*

The opposite of *doughnut*? Wait
A minute while I meditate.
This isn't easy. Ah, I've found it!
A cookie with a hole around it.

What is the opposite of *two*?
A lonely me, a lonely you.

The opposite of a *cloud* could be
A white reflection in the sea,
Or a huge blueness in the air,
Caused by a cloud's not being there.

The opposite of *opposite*?
That's much too difficult. I quit.

Richard Wilbur

In the list below, underline the words that can have **opposites**, and draw a ring around those that cannot. Then write down the underlined words and their **opposites**.

far   (door)   (blue)   wrong   (grass)   quickly   (pencil)   light

happy   (fridge)   (ten)   (town)   small   (computer)   (duck)

far – near, wrong – right, quickly – slowly, light – heavy or dark, happy – sad, small – big

Now look at the words you have ringed. Pick three, and make up **words** or **phrases** that could be "joke" **opposites** for them. Write your "joke" **opposites** and your reasons below.

door – wall (a wall is what is left if you have no door!)

Answers may vary

You may have found words that cannot even have "joke" **opposites**. Write them here.

The activities on this page focus on opposites. If your child comes up with justifiable opposites that are not included here, you could discuss the validity of the concept of opposites (which is the theme of the poem).

Spoonerisms

Kinquering congs is a well-known example of a **spoonerism**. W. A. Spooner from Oxford, England, accidentally "invented" spoonerisms: he often mixed up the sounds at the beginning of his words.

What did W. A. Spooner mean to say instead of kinquering congs?

Conquering kings

Here are some modern **spoonerisms** for you to "translate" into English – take care with the spelling! D

Did you hear the roar-bell ding?

Did you hear the doorbell ring?

Don't forget to dock the law!

Don't forget to lock the door!

We had thick frog last fiday.

We had thick fog last Friday.

Do you like to bead in red?

Do you like to read in bed?

I can fee my sootprints!

I can see my footprints!

I caught a ban of lemon drink.

I bought a can of lemon drink.

Can you think of any **spoonerisms** yourself? Write them here.

Answers may vary

This page introduces your child to a fun way of playing with sounds and spellings – the spoonerism. Help your child to use a dictionary to check any words that he or she cannot spell.

Malapropisms

Mrs. Malaprop is a character in a play by R. B. Sheridan. She often gets her words mixed up, using a word that sounds almost, but not quite, like the correct one. For instance, she says the word **allegory** when she means to say **alligator**!

Look up the word **allegory** in the dictionary, then explain the obvious difference between **allegory** and **alligator**. D

Answers may vary

Here are some **malapropisms** for you to correct – draw a ring around the word that is used incorrectly, then rewrite the sentence using the correct word. D

There are three (angels) in a triangle.

There are three angles in a triangle.

We decided to sign the (partition)

We decided to sign the petition.

I am pleased to (except) this prize.

I am pleased to accept this prize.

The brakes on a bike work by (fraction)

The brakes on a bike work by friction.

The (jugular) prepared to pounce.

The jaguar prepared to pounce.

Now find the meanings of the words you ringed, and write them here. D

Answers may vary

These exercises provide practice with words that sound similar but are spelt differently. Again, it may be helpful for your child to use a dictionary to check the spellings or meanings of words. Remember to praise correct answers.

Inventing words

Use a **dictionary** to complete these **definitions**. D

A micro chip is a very small chip of silicone.

A microprocessor is a circuit inside a computer

A microclimate is the climate of a very small area.

A microorganism is a very small living thing.

An instrument used to look at very small objects is a microscope

Find three more words beginning with the **prefix** micro- and explain their meanings. D

A micro .... is ....

A micro .... is ....

A micro .... is ....

Now make up some new "micro" words, and **define** them. For example, a microsnack is a snack that is too small to be satisfying but too tasty to resist.

Complete these **definitions**. D

A mega byte is a very large unit of computer memory.

A megaphone is a funnel to amplify voice

A megamouth is a shark with a very large mouth

A megalopolis is a group of large towns

A megalith is a very large stone or rock.

Now make up some "mega" words, and **define** them. For example, a megamouse is an extra-large mouse from the planet Megary.

On this page, your child experiments with inventing and building words. You could extend this idea by asking your child to think up a word game based on invented words or to write a dictionary of invented words.

Similes

Some **similes**, such as "like a house on fire", are called **cliches** because they are so overused that they have very little impact. It is a good idea to use new **similes** in your writing, as they attract interest and help your reader to imagine what you are describing. **Remember**: A **simile** is something compared with something else to create an image in the reader's mind. It usually includes the words **like** or **as**.

Practise writing new **similes** by thinking of original comparisons for these **adjectives**.

as light as .._a petal_......................   as dry as ....

as good as ....   as heavy as ....

as dull as ....   as pretty as ....

as clean as ....   as big as ....

as quick as ....   as rich as ....

Complete these sentences by thinking of **similes** for the **verbs**.

He crawled like _a snail_..........................

The athlete ran like ....

The small boat sank like ....

It rained like ....

Complete these sentences by thinking of **similes** for the **nouns**.

The heat was like _a blazing bonfire_

The thick mud felt as if ....

The black smoke smelt like ....

The music she played sounded like ....

The fresh water tasted like ....

The overgrown garden looked as if ....

Answers may vary

These activities encourage your child to think of original comparisons and to avoid overused expressions. There are no right or wrong answers to these questions – accept any original similes as long as they include the words *like* or *as*.

Metaphors

Read this **poem** aloud.

What is the Sun?

the Sun is an orange dinghy
    sailing across a calm sea

it is a gold coin
    dropped down a drain in Heaven

the Sun is a yellow beach ball
    kicked high into the summer sky

it is a red thumb-print
    on a sheet of pale blue paper

the Sun is a milk bottle's gold top
    floating in a puddle

Wes Magee

How many **metaphors** for the Sun can you find in this **poem**? Make a list of them below. **Remember**: A **metaphor** is something described as if it were something else. It is like a simile but does not include the words **like** or **as**.

an orange dinghy, _a gold chain, a yellow beachball, a red thumb-print,_
a milk bottle's gold top

Rewrite one of the five **verses**, and change the **metaphor** to a **simile**. To do this, you only need to add one word.

eg the Sun is like an orange dinghy
sailing across a calm sea

Pick a **verse** from the **poem**, and write a short paragraph explaining what is meant by the description of the Sun.

....
....
....

Which of the **metaphors** in the poem seems most effective to you? Why?

....
....

This page helps your child to appreciate how metaphor works and to differentiate between metaphor and simile. Again, the questions are open-ended – accept any answers that can be sensibly argued from the poem.

Write your own metaphors

Use the pattern of the **poem** on page 10 to write a **poem** of your own that includes **metaphors**. Choose one of the **titles** below or make up your own.

What is a cloud?

What is the sea?

What is the Moon?

What is ....? (your choice)

....(title)

....
....
....
....
....
....
....
....
....

Answers may vary

Here the task is to write a poem using metaphors. This activity gives your child practice in finding effective metaphors for use in his or her own writing. Encourage your child to read the finished poem to you. Remember to praise his or her efforts.

Sentence-building

Simple sentences can be made longer by adding **clauses**. A **compound sentence** consists of two or more clauses of equal importance. A **complex sentence** consists of one or more main clauses and another clause that needs the others to make complete sense.

Jack heard a strange noise. (**simple sentence** – one clause)

Jack heard a strange noise, and we were scared. (**compound sentence** – two simple sentences joined by **and** to make two equally important clauses)

Jack heard a strange noise, and we were scared when he told us about it. (**complex sentence** – there is a third clause, which needs the others to make complete sense.)

Build these **simple sentences** into **compound sentences** by adding a clause of equal importance. The first one has been done for you.
Remember: A **clause** is a group of words that includes a verb.

The dog barked.

The dog barked but we didn't hear anything.

The rain fell.

....

She ran across the park.

....

The computer crashed.

....

Now build your **compound sentences** into **complex sentences** by adding another clause.

The dog barked but we didn't hear anything because
the television was too loud.

....

Answers may vary

On this page your child learns how sentences can be made longer by the addition of clauses. Check that your child understands the examples on this page, particularly the point that every clause must contain a verb.

Different types of writing

The text extracts below could have come from any of the following types of writing:
instructions, explanations, poems, folk tales, novels, information or **arguments**.
Read each extract, then decide which type of writing it is.

Stop! Before you throw anything away, think ...	instruction
The old miller knew he had not long to live so ...	folktale
If the water is added gradually to the powder in the test tube, then ...	information
Thus, the water evaporates and returns to the atmosphere.	explanation
That peculiar person from Putney!	poem
The day was warm, though cloudy, and I noticed a strange scent in the air ...	novel
a blue-grey day a Saturday	poem
Surely you must realise that ...	argument
Add the beaten egg ...	instruction
The second planet from the Sun is called ...	information

Choose one of the above extracts that comes from a **fiction** book. Imagine what the rest of the paragraph might look like, and write a draft version on a separate sheet of paper. Then write the finished paragraph below.
Remember: Fiction means text that was invented by the writer.

Answers may vary

If you want to, do the same thing by choosing an extract from a **non-fiction** book. Write the paragraph on a separate sheet of paper.
Remember: Non-fiction means that the information in the piece of writing is factual.

This page helps your child to recognise the features of different genres (types) of text, and to use them in his or her own writing. Your child's paragraph should display elements of a particular style of fiction or non-fiction writing.

Comparing poems

Read these two **poems** aloud, listening to the **rhythms** and the **sounds**.

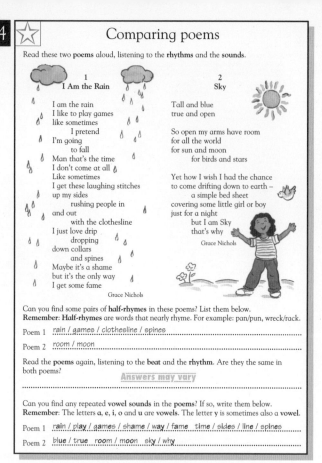

1
I Am the Rain

I am the rain
I like to play games
like sometimes
  I pretend
I'm going
  to fall
Man that's the time
I don't come at all
Like sometimes
I get these laughing stitches
up my sides
  rushing people in
and out
  with the clothesline
I just love drip
  dropping
down collars
  and spines
Maybe it's a shame
but it's the only way
I get some fame

Grace Nichols

2
Sky

Tall and blue
true and open

So open my arms have room
for all the world
for sun and moon
  for birds and stars

Yet how I wish I had the chance
to come drifting down to earth –
a simple bed sheet
covering some little girl or boy
just for a night
but I am Sky
that's why

Grace Nichols

Can you find some pairs of **half-rhymes** in these poems? List them below.
Remember: Half-rhymes are words that nearly rhyme. For example: pan/pun, wreck/rack.

Poem 1   rain / games / clothesline / spines

Poem 2   room / moon

Read the **poems** again, listening to the **beat** and the **rhythm**. Are they the same in both poems?

Answers may vary

Can you find any repeated **vowel sounds** in the poems? If so, write them below.
Remember: The letters a, e, i, o and u are **vowels**. The letter y is sometimes also a **vowel**.

Poem 1   rain / play / games / shame / way / fame   time / sides / line / spines

Poem 2   blue / true   room / moon   sky / why

Two modern poems on the theme of the weather are presented on this page. Encourage your child to read the poems out loud and to listen for the rhyming words.

Investigating poems

Reread the **poems** on page 14. What do you notice about the **punctuation** in both poems?
There is very little punctuation – mainly capital letters and apostrophes.

What do you notice about the way the poems are **set out**? Look where the lines start.
The words on some lines start midway along the line.

Who or what is speaking in poem 1?
The rain is speaking in poem 1.

Who or what is speaking in poem 2?
The sky is speaking in poem 2.

Can these poems be placed under the same heading? If so, what might that heading be?
These poems could be described as poems about things in nature.

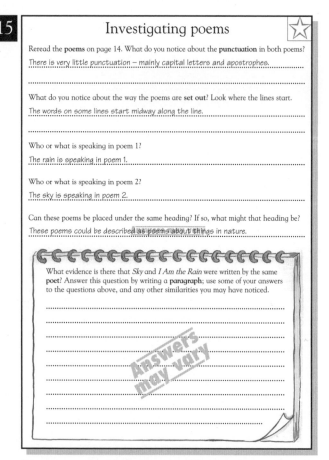

What evidence is there that *Sky* and *I Am the Rain* were written by the same **poet**? Answer this question by writing a **paragraph**; use some of your answers to the questions above, and any other similarities you may have noticed.

Answers may vary

These exercises help your child to compare two poems by the same writer and to reveal similar techniques and themes. Talk to your child about the poet's use of personification (treating things that are not human as if they were people).

Fast fact-finding

Read the passage below.

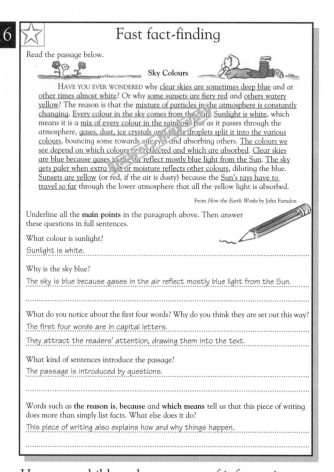

Sky Colours

HAVE YOU EVER WONDERED why clear skies are sometimes deep blue and at other times almost white? Or why some sunsets are fiery red and others watery yellow? The reason is that the mixture of particles in the atmosphere is constantly changing. Every colour in the sky comes from the Sun. Sunlight is white, which means it is a mix of every colour in the rainbow, but as it passes through the atmosphere, gases, dust, ice crystals and water droplets split it into the various colours, bouncing some towards our eyes and absorbing others. The colours we see depend on which colours are reflected and which are absorbed. Clear skies are blue because gases in the air reflect mostly blue light from the Sun. The sky gets paler when extra dust or moisture reflects other colours, diluting the blue. Sunsets are yellow (or red, if the air is dusty) because the Sun's rays have to travel so far through the lower atmosphere that all the yellow light is absorbed.

From *How the Earth Works* by John Farndon

Underline all the **main points** in the paragraph above. Then answer these questions in full sentences.

What colour is sunlight?
Sunlight is white.

Why is the sky blue?
The sky is blue because gases in the air reflect mostly blue light from the Sun.

What do you notice about the first four words? Why do you think they are set out this way?
The first four words are in capital letters.
They attract the readers' attention, drawing them into the text.

What kind of sentences introduce the passage?
The passage is introduced by questions.

Words such as **the reason is**, **because** and **which means** tell us that this piece of writing does more than simply list facts. What else does it do?
This piece of writing also explains how and why things happen.

Here your child reads a passage of information text. The questions help your child to identify the main facts and to analyse the way in which the information is presented. Check that your child writes his or her answers in complete sentences.

Following instructions ☆

Read the following piece of writing.

Experiment: Red and Blue Skies

It is not always easy to believe that all the colours in the sky come from the different way particles in the atmosphere reflect and absorb sunlight. But you can demonstrate it for yourself with this very simple experiment. The effects are quite subtle, and not always easy to see, so you need to conduct the experiment in a very dark room. <u>Fill a straight glass with cold water, then <u>add half a teaspoonful of milk. Now <u>try shining the torch at the glass from different angles and <u>watch how the colour of the milky water changes</u> very slightly. <u>Hold the torch close to the glass</u> for a better effect. <u>Add another half-teaspoonful of milk</u> and <u>repeat</u>. Finally, <u>add a full teaspoonful of milk, and <u>try shining the torch at the glass from a variety of different angles</u>.

From How the Earth Works by John Farndon

Read through the text again, underlining the actual **instructions**. On a separate sheet of paper, draw a **flow chart** that shows the **instructions** in the correct order.

Try the **experiment** yourself, then make **notes** under these headings.

Equipment/materials needed *straight glass of cold water, 2 tsps milk,*
teaspoon, torch

What I did *filled straight glass with cold water, added half a teaspoonful of milk*
shone torch at glass from different angles

What I saw *Answers may vary*

What I learnt from the experiment *Answers may vary*

The activities on this page and the following one focus on the instructions for a scientific experiment. The exercises are designed to give your child practice in formal writing. Encourage your child to do the actual experiment.

Reporting

Write a brief factual **report** on the experiment featured on page 17.
Remember: Use straightforward statements in the passive voice when writing a **report**. For example, write **the milk is mixed with the water** rather than **I mixed the milk with the water.**

Answers may vary

Do you think this old **saying** is likely to be true?

Red sky at night, shepherd's delight –
Red sky in the morning, shepherd's warning.

Answers may vary

In your own words, write an **explanation** of why the sky appears to change colour and what causes this. Before you write, try to find out more information. Use **reference books**, **CD-ROMs** or the **Internet**. Then compare your findings with the information on page 16. Don't forget to say where you got your information from. Begin here, and continue on a separate sheet of paper.

Answers may vary

Check that your child's report is written in a formal style, suitable for a science notebook and that it is expressed mainly in the passive voice. The explanation should be concise and informative and contain a list of the reference sources.

Paragraphs and punctuation ☆

Rewrite the following passage in **paragraphs**, **punctuating** it and changing small letters into capital letters where necessary.
Remember: Paragraphs separate ideas, themes or instructions. Without paragraphs, writing can be difficult to understand.

rainbows
my heart leaps up when i behold a rainbow in the sky wrote william wordsworth the famous poet and most of us share his feelings when we are lucky enough to see a rainbow there is an old saying that a pot of gold is buried at the end of the rainbow but have you ever tried to reach a rainbows end of course its impossible because a rainbow is really just the result of the raindrops refracting and reflecting light from our sun there are seven colours in the rainbow red orange yellow green blue indigo and violet

"My heart leaps up when I behold a rainbow in the sky," wrote William Wordsworth, the famous English poet, and most of us share his feelings when we are lucky enough to see a rainbow.

There is an old saying that a pot of gold is buried at the end of the rainbow, but have you ever tried to reach a rainbow's end? Of course it's impossible, because a rainbow is really just the result of the raindrops refracting and reflecting light from our Sun.

There are seven colours in the rainbow: red, orange, yellow, green, blue, indigo and violet.

Rewrite this section of a **play script** as a **story**. Use **paragraphs** and **speech marks**. Write on a separate sheet of paper, and continue the story, if you wish.
Remember: When writing **direct speech** (dialogue), start a new paragraph each time the speaker changes.

"It's raining again, but the sun is shining as well," said Nick.
"I think we should go swimming anyway," said Sophie.
"We might get wet ... let's wait a bit longer," suggested Nick.
"We can't swim without getting wet, Nick. What difference does it make?" Sophie asked.
"Hey!" exclaimed Nick.
"What is it?" asked Sophie.
"Look – a rainbow over the beach!" cried Nick.
"Quick, get your spade – we'll be rich!" exclaimed Sophie.

There are many slight variations possible in the answers to these punctuation exercises. Your child may realise that there are creative choices in the use of punctuation, but a knowledge of the basic rules should be evident in his or her writing.

Old text

Read this **extract** carefully, then answer, in full sentences, the questions that follow.

For some minutes Alice stood without speaking, looking out in all directions over the country – and a most curious country it was. There were a number of tiny little brooks running straight across it from side to side, and the ground between was divided up into squares by a number of little green hedges, that reached from brook to brook.
"I declare it's marked out just like a large chess-board!" Alice said at last. "There ought to be some men moving about somewhere – and so there are!" she added in a tone of delight, and her heart began to beat quick with excitement as she went on. "It's a great huge game of chess that's being played – all over the world – if this *is* the world at all, you know. Oh, what fun it is! How I *wish* I was one of them! I wouldn't mind being a Pawn, if only I might join – though of course I should *like* to be a Queen, best."
She glanced rather shyly at the real Queen as she said this, but her companion only smiled pleasantly, and said "That's easily managed. You can be the White Queen's Pawn, if you like, as Lily's too young to play; and you're in the Second Square to begin with: when you get to the Eighth Square you'll be a Queen –" Just at this moment, somehow or other, they began to run.

From Through the Looking Glass by Lewis Carroll

Who is the **main character** in this story?
The main character in this story is Alice.

Where is this episode **set**? Describe the **setting** in your own words.
The episode is set in a strange country with streams and hedges forming squares like those on a chessboard.

Does Alice expect to enjoy this part of her adventure or not? How can you tell?
Yes. Alice sounds delighted and is very excited about joining in the game.

Why would Alice rather be a queen than a pawn?
The queen is far more important and powerful than a pawn.

Which side is Alice about to play for?
Alice is about to play for the white team.

Can you find any words or phrases to suggest that this was written a long time ago?
Phrases that suggest this was written a long time ago include: a most curious country it was; I declare; Oh what fun it is!; How I wish I was one of them.

On this page and the following one, your child compares two extracts from children's books. They are from different periods in time, but share a similar theme. Check that your child writes his or her answers in full sentences.

New text

Read this **extract** carefully, then answer in full sentences, the questions that follow.

They followed, running again. Once inside the house, with its maze of corridors, they could lose her. But there she was – they heard her first, those dragging footsteps. Then, hurrying, they saw her blue cloak, fair head. She pushed a huge panelled door and passed through, leaving it open behind her. They reached it and peered in just in time to see Sarah passing through yet another door on the far side of a room that was evidently part of the main house. There was heavy, gleaming furniture, walls lined with gilt-framed pictures, richly draped windows. Minty set off across it …

They were through the second door now, and into an amazing crimson.

'Cor!' Tom was awestruck. 'Red Drawing Room, this is! Heard about it? 'Cor! Ain't it just red?'

It was. Carpet, walls, hangings smouldered, blazed. The very air breathed red.

Sarah had vanished. Minty crossed the room and came into a vast light entrance hall. There, on the great black and white diamonds of the floor, was that small blue figure, a chess piece.

At that moment there came other footsteps, a clatter and rattle. Sarah stopped in her tracks, Minty and Tom stiffened.

From Moondial by Helen Cresswell

Where is this episode **set**? Describe the **setting** in your own words.
The episode is set inside a big, old house.
Most of it is set inside a red drawing room.

Name the three characters in this part of the story.
The three characters in this part of the story are Sarah, Minty and Tom.

Why do you think Sarah is described as "a chess piece"?
Sarah is described as "a chess piece" because she is standing on a floor that looks like a chessboard.

Have you heard the saying "a pawn in the game"? What does it mean? [D]
If someone is described as being "a pawn in the game", it means that he or she has very little control over what happens.

Is the next part of this story likely to be funny or threatening? How can you tell?
The next part of the story is likely to be threatening. The noises are ominous, and the characters seem tense.

Is this extract more modern than the extract on page 20? Give reasons for your answer.
This extract is more modern than the one on page 21. Although the character Tom uses old-fashioned phrases, the descriptive language is modern.

This page features a modern extract that shares a similar theme to the older extract on page 20. Talk about the text together before your child answers the questions. Check your child's handwriting, and point out areas that need further practice.

Comparing texts

Use the following questions to help you **plan** a **comparison** of the **extracts** on pages 20 and 21.

Underline the words of the **narrator** in both extracts. Write a sentence comparing them.
Answers may vary

Draw a ring around the **conversations** in both extracts. What differences can you see?
Answers may vary

Compare the **styles** of the two authors (their particular way of writing).
Answers may vary

Which of these terms could be used for the stories: **traditional**, **fantasy**, **novel**, **adventure**, autobiography, romance, historical?
fantasy, novel, adventure

Would you like to read more of either of these books? Which one and why?
Answers may vary

Now write a **summary** of your **views** on these two extracts. Make sure you base your arguments on the words in the text. Remember to use **paragraphs**. Begin here, and continue on a separate sheet of paper.

Comparing the styles of two writers

Answers may vary

This page enables your child to write in detail about his or her response to the texts on pages 20 and 21. It may be helpful to talk about the questions with your child: this will help provoke the sort of discussion that takes place in a classroom.

Reported speech

Rewrite the following text in **reported speech**. It has been started for you. Continue on a separate sheet of paper if necessary.
Remember: **Reported speech** reports what the characters have said, rather than quoting their actual words. **Reported speech** is in the **past tense** and has no speech marks.

The Queen propped her up against a tree, and said kindly, "You may rest a little, now." Alice looked round her in great surprise. "Why, I do believe we've been under this tree the whole time! Everything's just as it was!"

"Of course it is," said the Queen: "what would you have it?"

"Well, in *our* country," said Alice, still panting a little, "you'd generally get to somewhere else – if you ran very fast for a long time, as we've been doing."

"A slow sort of country!" said the Queen. "Now, *here*, you see, it takes all the running *you* can do, to keep in the same place. If you want to get somewhere else, you must run at least twice as fast as that!"

"I'd rather not try, please!" said Alice. "I'm quite content to stay here – only I *am* so hot and thirsty!"

"I know what *you'd* like!" the Queen said good-naturedly, taking a little box out of her pocket. "Have a biscuit?"

From Through the Looking Glass by Lewis Carroll

The Queen propped her up against a tree and told her kindly that she could rest a little. Alice looked around her and said with surprise, that she believed they had been under that tree all the time and everything had stayed just as it was. The Queen replied that of course it had and asked Alice what else she would want it to be. Alice explained, still panting slightly, that in her country people generally reached somewhere else if they ran fast for a long time as they had. The Queen declared that Alice's must be a slow sort of country. In hers, you had to run as fast as you could just to stay in one place and you needed to run twice as fast to get anywhere else. Alice said that she would rather not try and she was happy to stay where she was except that she was hot and thirsty. The Queen said she knew what Alice would like and asked her if she wanted a biscuit.

Most authors use a mixture of **reported** and **direct** speech. Why do you think they do this?
Using reported speech can help the story to flow and save space. Direct speech gives a sense of "being there".

This page provides your child with practice in converting direct speech into reported speech and examines the stylistic reasons for choosing one form or the other. Check that your child's rewriting of the passage is grammatically correct.

Reading a dialect

Read this **extract** aloud.

I'm Bell Teesdale. I'm a lad. I'm eight …

All down Mallerstang there's becks running down off the fell. It's bonny. Down off the sharp scales, dry in summer till one single drop of rain sends them running and rushing and tumbling down the fell-side like threads of silk. Like cobwebs. And when the wind blows across the dale these becks gasp, and they rise up on theirselves like the wild horses in Wateryat Bottom. They rise up on their hind legs. Or like smoke blowing, like ever so many bonfires, not water at all, all smoking in the wind between Castledale and the Moorcock toward Wensleydale. It's bonny.

And townsfolk come looking at all this now where once they only went to the Lake District over the west. Renting and leasing they come. Talking south. "Why'd they come?" I ask our grandad who's leased the farm house he used to live in (my gran died). "There's not owt for 'em here. What's use of a farm to them? Just for sitting in. Never a thing going on."

"Resting," says my grandad. "They take 'em for resting in after London."

From The Hollow Land by Jane Gardam

What is a **dialect**? How does it differ from standard English?
A dialect is a form of language spoken in a specific region. Some words and phrases have different meanings from standard English. Words are often pronounced differently

Unless you live in the part of England where this text is set, you probably found this difficult to read aloud. Why? [D]
It is difficult to pronounce some of the unfamiliar words and phrases.

Can you give the standard English words for these words: beck, fell, bonny, scales, theirselves? [D]
The standard English words are stream, mountain, pretty, steep slopes, themselves.

What do you think the following local expressions mean?
It's bonny It's pretty.
There's not owt for 'em here There is nothing to interest them here.

Here the task is for your child to read and answer questions about a passage of text written in a local dialect. Your child may find some, but not all, of the dialect words in a dictionary. Encourage him or her to guess a word's meaning from its context.

Reading and understanding

Read this **extract** from the same collection of stories as the **extract** on page 24.

James sat on another slope beneath a crag with a book open on his knees and in turn watched a figure below him – old Grandfather Hewitson who was parading along the dry bed of a beck, slashing thistles.

The four figures were the only signs of life for miles. It was a hot, still day. Light Trees was the only building in sight. No smoke rose from its chimney. Far away the Lake District mountains swam with heat.

"However long is it going to be?" said Harry. "He could sit there all day. And when he does get hungry and go in, there's still your grandad."

"You'd think he'd know every word of that book by now," said Bell. "Does he do owt else but take exams?"

From The Hollow Land by Jane Gardam

Is Bell the **narrator** in this **extract**? How can you tell?
I can tell that Bell is not the narrator because it would say "I said" rather than "said Bell" if Bell was telling the story.

In which season of the year is this story **set**? How can you tell?
The story is set in the summer. I can tell it's summer from the words "It was a hot, still day" and "swam with heat".

Are there any particularly **local words** in this **extract**? Are any of them the same as in the passage on page 24?
The word "owt" is a local word that appears in both passages.

What type of writing do you think these **extracts** come from? Choose from these: **historical adventure, fantasy, adventure, anecdote, biography, science fiction.** ☐D
anecdote

Now choose a landscape (town or country) that you know well, and write a **description** of it to form the **setting** for a story.
....
Answers may vary
....

This page helps your child to appreciate the difference between a dialect and standard English and to recognise the style of an individual writer. Check that your child writes his or her answers in complete sentences.

A questionnaire

Complete this brief **questionnaire** about your reading.

Fiction

Tick the types of **fiction** that you enjoy reading.

novels ☐   short stories ☐   science fiction ☐   historical ☐

adventure ☐   mystery ☐   fantasy ☐   others ....

My favourite **authors** are ....

My favourite **fiction** titles are ....
....

Poetry

Tick the types of **poems** that you enjoy.

ballads ☐   haiku ☐   cinquain ☐   free verse ☐

limericks ☐   shape poems ☐   others ....

My favourite **poets** are ....

My favourite **poems** are ....
....

Non-fiction

Tick the types of **non-fiction** that you enjoy reading.

sports ☐   games ☐   hobbies ☐   animal care ☐   computers ☐

science ☐   art ☐   music ☐   TV, film, etc. ☐   others ....

My favourite **non-fiction** titles are ....
....

Now write more about your favourite types of reading on a separate sheet of paper. Try to persuade other people of your age to read the books or poems that you enjoy the most. Take care with your **punctuation, spelling** and **handwriting.**

On this page your child is asked to analyse his or her reading preferences and to write persuasively for a particular readership. Encourage your child to write in paragraphs and to check his or her finished writing for spelling and punctuation errors.

Prefixes

Read the following list of **prefixes,** then write the **prefixes** in **alphabetical order.**
Remember: A prefix is a group of letters added to the beginning of a word to change its meaning.

post-   ante-   kilo-   pro-   geo-   bio-   retro-   vari-   zoo-   multi-
hydro-   sub-   extra-   ultra-   fore-   peri-   iso-   contra-   thermo-

ante-, bio-, contra-, extra-, fore-, geo-, hydro-, iso-, kilo-, multi-, peri-, post-, pro-, retro-, sub-, thermo-, ultra-, vari-, zoo-

Use a **dictionary** to find a word beginning with each of the **prefixes** listed above. Write each word in a sentence that shows its meaning. ☐D

antechamber: We came to a small antechamber before entering the main hall.
....
Answers may vary

The activities on this page focus on the use of prefixes and help to extend vocabulary through word-building. There is also a chance to practise alphabetical ordering. Check that your child's sentences use the completed words correctly.

Suffixes

Follow the instructions below for each of the words in this list.

artist	importance	stationary	changeable	lioness
sorrowful	telegraph	clarify	advertise	magnetism
senseless	skilfully	happiness	headship	attitude
motion	cruelty	otherwise	pomposity	

1 Write the word in the first column of the **chart.**
2 Decide which part of the word is its **suffix**, and write it in the second column.
3 Think of another word with the same **suffix**, and check its spelling in a dictionary. ☐D
4 Write the new word in the third column of the **chart.**
Remember: A **suffix** is a group of letters added to the end of a word to change its meaning.

artist	-ist	chemist
importance	-ance	
stationary	-ary	
changeable	-able	
lioness	-ess	
sorrowful	-ful	
telegraph	-graph	
clarify	-ify	
advertise	-ise	
magnetism	-ism	
senseless	-less	
skilfully	-ly	
happiness	-ness	
headship	-ship	
attitude	-ude	
motion	-ion	
cruelty	-ty	
otherwise	-wise	
pomposity	-ity	

Answers may vary

This page extends your child's word-building skills with practice in the use of suffixes. In the last column of the chart, accept any word with the correct suffix.

Joining sentences

The **sentences** below are about the game of chess, but they are in the wrong order. Read through the **sentences** and decide on the best order.

Computers play chess. Chess remains popular today. There are sixteen pieces on each side. Chess is a game for two people. "Checkmate" means that the king cannot move without being taken by another piece. The board and the pieces can be in any two contrasting colours. Pieces move in different ways. Computers sometimes beat human champions. Chess is played on a chequered board. It seems complicated at first. Each side has one king, one queen, two knights, two bishops, two rooks and eight pawns. The board is usually black and white. The game ends when one of the kings is "checkmated". Experts improve their game by learning special patterns of moves. Chess is a very old game.

Write the sentences in order here.

1 Chess is a very old game.
2 Chess remains popular today.
3 Computers play chess.
4 Computers sometimes beat human champions.
5 Chess is a game for two people.
6 Chess is played on a chequered board.
7 The board is usually black and white.
8 The board and the pieces can be any two contrasting colours.
9 There are sixteen pieces on each side.
10 Each side has one king, one queen, two knights, two bishops, two rooks and eight pawns.
11 Pieces move in different ways.
12 It seems complicated at first.
13 Experts improve their game by learning special patterns of moves.
14 "Checkmate" means that the king cannot move without being taken by another piece.
15 The game ends when one of the kings is "checkmated".

All these **sentences** about chess are very short. **Join** some of the **sentences** to make the piece of writing read more fluently. You may need to add, remove or change some words, but make sure you keep all the main ideas. Write out your **sentences** on a separate sheet of paper.

Here your child practises organising information. Remind your child about some connecting words and phrases that he or she could use. Your child's finished writing should read fluently and contain all the main points from the original.

Active and passive

Active sentences describe an action done **by the subject**.
  I directed the award-winning film. (an **active** sentence)
Passive sentences describe an action done **to the subject**.
  The award-winning film was directed by me. (a **passive** sentence)

Change these sentences from **passive** to **active**.

The match was won by our team.
Our team won the match.

The winning goal was scored by Rachel.
Rachel scored the winning goal.

The party was enjoyed by all my friends.
All my friends enjoyed the party.

Jack was stung by an unusual insect.
An unusual insect stung Jack.

Now change these sentences from **active** to **passive**.

Aliens invade our planet.
Our planet is invaded by aliens.

Leonardo da Vinci painted the *Mona Lisa*.
The Mona Lisa was painted by Leonardo da Vinci.

The team dislike the group leader.
The group leader is disliked by the team.

The hero piloted his craft with great skill.
The hero's craft was piloted with great skill.

A hurricane struck the town.
The town was struck by a hurricane.

Here the task is to change a sentence from active to passive and *vice versa*. Check that your child understands the difference between the active and passive voices and can use them confidently. It may help if you think up practice sentences together.

Colons, semicolons and dashes

Punctuation can be used to connect groups of words. The **punctuation marks** that do this are: the **colon** (:), the **semicolon** (;) and the **dash** (–).

Read each sentence below, and write another sentence using the same **punctuation marks**.
Remember:
• A **colon** is used to introduce a list, a quotation or a second clause that makes the first clause easier to understand. (A clause is a group of words with a verb in it.)
• A **semicolon** is used to link complete clauses that are too closely related to separate with a full stop.
  It can also be used to separate items in a list that already has commas in it.
• A **dash** can be used to separate a comment from the rest of a sentence. It makes a stronger break than a comma and is less formal than brackets.

Bring these things with you: a jumper, your swimsuit, your lunch and your bus fare.
....
....

It was Shakespeare's Juliet who asked: "What's in a name?"
....

The match was abandoned: rain poured down.
....
....

We had to stop playing; we went to Matt's house.
....

I bought a kilo of big, juicy apples; two large, ripe lemons; a grapefruit and a punnet of delicious, sweet-smelling strawberries.
....
....
....

The weather is lovely – wish you were here!
....

Answers may vary

These sentences help your child explore the use of colons, semicolons and dashes. Children often find these sophisticated punctuation marks very difficult to use, so you may need to offer help. Accept any sentences with the correct punctuation.

Connectives

Here are some one-word **connectives**.

and	but	when	because
so	for	as	though

Choose a different one of these **connectives** to link each of the paired sentences below.
Remember: Connectives are words or phrases that link together different parts of a text. Connectives that link sentences, clauses or parts of phrases are called **conjunctions**.

I fell over. I hurt my knee. I fell over and I hurt my knee.

The game ended. The referee blew his whistle. The game ended when the referee blew his whistle.

She couldn't ride her bike. It had a puncture. She couldn't ride her bike because it had a puncture.

I couldn't spell that word. I fetched the dictionary. I couldn't spell that word so I fetched the dictionary.

We arrived on time. The train was delayed. We arrived on time but the train was delayed.

Here are some **words** and **phrases** that can also be used as **connectives**.

also	however	this means	for example	as this

Fit the **connectives** above into the spaces in these three paragraphs.

Many kinds of words can be used to connect ideas in a piece of writing. For example, pronouns, adverbs and conjunctions are all useful.

This means that we can make our writing more varied and more interesting to read. Also, the words we choose can help us to make our meaning clearer to our readers.

However, we should try not to use too many of these connectives in a short piece, as this can make our sentences long and confusing.

Here your child practises using connectives (joining words, phrases or clauses). As your child works through the final exercise, check that he or she understands the meaning of the passage. Don't forget to praise your child's efforts.

Following instructions

Read the following piece of writing.

Experiment: Red and Blue Skies

It is not always easy to believe that all the colours in the sky come from the different way particles in the atmosphere reflect and absorb sunlight. But you can demonstrate it for yourself with this very simple experiment. The effects are quite subtle, and not always easy to see, so you need to conduct the experiment in a very dark room. Fill a straight glass with cold water, then add half a teaspoonful of milk. Now try shining the torch at the glass from different angles and watch how the colour of the milky water changes very slightly. Hold the torch close to the glass for a better effect. Add another half-teaspoonful of milk and repeat. Finally, add a full teaspoonful of milk, and try shining the torch at the glass from a variety of different angles.

From *How the Earth Works* by John Farndon

Read through the text again, underlining the actual **instructions**. On a separate sheet of paper, draw a **flow chart** that shows the **instructions** in the correct order.

Try the **experiment** yourself, then make **notes** under these headings.

Equipment/materials needed ....
....

What I did ....
....
....

What I saw ....
....

What I learnt from the experiment ....
....
....

Reporting

Write a brief factual **report** on the experiment featured on page 17.
Remember: Use straightforward statements in the passive voice when writing a **report**.
For example, write **the milk is mixed with the water** rather than **I mixed the milk with the water**.

....
....
....
....
....
....
....
....

Do you think this old **saying** is likely to be true?

Red sky at night, shepherd's delight –
Red sky in the morning, shepherd's warning.

....
....

In your own words, write an **explanation** of why the sky appears to change colour and
what causes this. Before you write, try to find out more information. Use **reference
books, CD-ROMs** or the **Internet**. Then compare your findings with the information
on page 16. Don't forget to say where you got your information from. Begin here, and
continue on a separate sheet of paper.

....
....
....
....
....

Paragraphs and punctuation

Rewrite the following passage in **paragraphs**, **punctuating** it and changing small letters into capital letters where necessary.

Remember: **Paragraphs** separate ideas, themes or instructions. Without paragraphs, writing can be difficult to understand.

rainbows

my heart leaps up when i behold a rainbow in the sky wrote william wordsworth the famous poet and most of us share his feelings when we are lucky enough to see a rainbow there is an old saying that a pot of gold is buried at the end of the rainbow but have you ever tried to reach a rainbows end of course its impossible because a rainbow is really just the result of the raindrops refracting and reflecting light from our sun there are seven colours in the rainbow red orange yellow green blue indigo and violet

....

....

....

....

....

....

....

....

Rewrite this section of a **play script** as a **story**. Use **paragraphs** and **speech marks**. Write on a separate sheet of paper, and continue the story, if you wish.

Remember: When writing **direct speech** (dialogue), start a new paragraph each time the speaker changes.

"It's raining again, but the sun is shining as well" said Nick.

"I think we should go swimming anyway" said Sophie.

"We might get wet ... let's wait a bit longer," suggested Nick.

"We can't swim without getting wet, Nick. What difference does it make?" Sophie asked.

"Hey!" exclaimed Nick.

"What is it?" asked Sophie.

"Look – a rainbow over the beach!" cried Nick.

"Quick, get your spade – we'll be rich!" exclaimed Sophie.

Old text

Read this **extract** carefully, then answer, in full sentences, the questions that follow.

For some minutes Alice stood without speaking, looking out in all directions over the country – and a most curious country it was. There were a number of tiny little brooks running straight across it from side to side, and the ground between was divided up into squares by a number of little green hedges, that reached from brook to brook.

"I declare it's marked out just like a large chess-board!" Alice said at last. "There ought to be some men moving about somewhere – and so there are!" she added in a tone of delight, and her heart began to beat quick with excitement as she went on. "It's a great huge game of chess that's being played – all over the world – if this *is* the world at all, you know. Oh, what fun it is! How I *wish* I was one of them! I wouldn't mind being a Pawn, if only I might join – though of course I should *like* to be a Queen, best."

She glanced rather shyly at the real Queen as she said this, but her companion only smiled pleasantly, and said "That's easily managed. You can be the White Queen's Pawn, if you like, as Lily's too young to play; and you're in the Second Square to begin with: when you get to the Eighth Square you'll be a Queen –" Just at this moment, somehow or other, they began to run.

From *Through the Looking Glass* by Lewis Carroll

Who is the **main character** in this story?

....

Where is this episode **set**? Describe the **setting** in your own words.

....

....

Does Alice expect to enjoy this part of her adventure or not? How can you tell?

....

....

Why would Alice rather be a queen than a pawn?

....

....

Which side is Alice about to play for?

....

Can you find any words or phrases to suggest that this was written a long time ago?

....

....

New text

Read this **extract** carefully, then answer in full sentences, the questions that follow.

They followed, running again. Once inside the house, with its maze of corridors, they could lose her. But there she was – they heard her first, those dragging footsteps. Then, hurrying, they saw her blue cloak, fair head. She pushed a huge panelled door and passed through, leaving it open behind her. They reached it and peered in just in time to see Sarah passing through yet another door on the far side of a room that was evidently part of the main house. There was heavy, gleaming furniture, walls lined with gilt-framed pictures, richly draped windows. Minty set off across it …

They were through the second door now, and into an amazing crimson. 'Cor!' Tom was awestruck. 'Red Drawing Room, this is! Heard about it! Cor! Ain't it just red?'

It was. Carpet, walls, hangings smouldered, blazed. The very air breathed red.

Sarah had vanished. Minty crossed the room and came into a vast light entrance hall. There, on the great black and white diamonds of the floor, was that small blue figure, a chess piece.

At that moment there came other footsteps, a clatter and rattle. Sarah stopped in her tracks, Minty and Tom stiffened.

From *Moondial* by Helen Cresswell

Where is this episode **set**? Describe the **setting** in your own words.

....

....

Name the three characters in this part of the story.

....

....

Why do you think Sarah is described as "a chess piece"?

....

....

Have you heard the saying "a pawn in the game"? What does it mean? D

....

....

Is the next part of this story likely to be funny or threatening? How can you tell?

....

....

Is this extract more modern than the extract on page 20? Give reasons for your answer.

....

....

Comparing texts

Use the following questions to help you **plan** a **comparison** of the **extracts** on pages 20 and 21.

Underline the words of the **narrator** in both extracts. Write a sentence comparing them.

....

....

Draw a ring around the **conversations** in both extracts. What differences can you see?

....

....

Compare the **styles** of the two authors (their particular way of writing).

....

....

Which of these terms could be used for the stories: **traditional**, **fantasy**, **novel**, **adventure**, **autobiography**, **romance**, **historical**?

....

....

Would you like to read more of either of these books? Which one and why?

....

....

Now write a **summary** of your **views** on these two extracts. Make sure you base your arguments on the words in the text. Remember to use **paragraphs**. Begin here, and continue on a separate sheet of paper.

Comparing the styles of two writers

....

....

....

....

....

Reported speech

Rewrite the following text in **reported speech**. It has been started for you. Continue on a separate sheet of paper if necessary.

Remember: **Reported speech** reports what the characters have said, rather than quoting their actual words. **Reported speech** is in the **past tense** and has no speech marks.

The Queen propped her up against a tree, and said kindly, "You may rest a little, now."

Alice looked round her in great surprise. "Why, I do believe we've been under this tree the whole time! Everything's just as it was!"

"Of course it is," said the Queen: "what would you have it?"

"Well, in *our* country," said Alice, still panting a little, "you'd generally get to somewhere else – if you ran very fast for a long time, as we've been doing."

"A slow sort of country!" said the Queen. "Now, *here*, you see, it takes all the running *you* can do, to keep in the same place. If you want to get somewhere else, you must run at least twice as fast as that!"

"I'd rather not try, please!" said Alice. "I'm quite content to stay here – only I *am* so hot and thirsty!"

"I know what *you'd* like!" the Queen said good-naturedly, taking a little box out of her pocket. "Have a biscuit?"

From *Through the Looking Glass* by Lewis Carroll

The Queen propped her up against a tree and told her kindly that she

....

....

....

....

....

....

....

....

....

Most authors use a mixture of **reported** and **direct speech**. Why do you think they do this?

....

....

Reading a dialect

Read this **extract** aloud.

I'm Bell Teesdale. I'm a lad. I'm eight ...

　　All down Mallerstang there's becks running down off the fell. It's bonny. Down off the sharp scales, dry in summer till one single drop of rain sends them running and rushing and tumbling down the fell-side like threads of silk. Like cobwebs. And when the wind blows across the dale these becks gasp, and they rise up on theirselves like the wild horses in Wateryat Bottom. They rise up on their hind legs. Or like smoke blowing, like ever so many bonfires, not water at all, all smoking in the wind between Castledale and the Moorcock toward Wensleydale. It's bonny.

　　And townsfolk come looking at all this now where once they only went to the Lake District over the west. Renting and leasing they come. Talking south. "Why'd they come?" I ask our grandad who's leased the farm house he used to live in (my gran died). "There's not owt for 'em here. What's use of a farm to them? Just for sitting in. Never a thing going on."

　　"Resting," says my grandad. "They take 'em for resting in after London."

From *The Hollow Land* by Jane Gardam

What is a **dialect**? How does it differ from standard English?

....

....

Unless you live in the part of England where this text is set, you probably found this difficult to read aloud. Why? D

....

....

Can you give the standard English words for these words: beck, fell, bonny, scales, theirselves? D

....

....

What do you think the following local expressions mean?

It's bonny ....

....

There's not owt for 'em here ....

....

Reading and understanding

Read this **extract** from the same collection of stories as the **extract** on page 24.

James sat on another slope beneath a crag with a book open on his knees and in turn watched a figure below him – old Grandfather Hewitson who was parading along the dry bed of a beck, slashing thistles.

The four figures were the only signs of life for miles. It was a hot, still day. Light Trees was the only building in sight. No smoke rose from its chimney. Far away the Lake District mountains swam with heat.

"However long is it going to be?" said Harry. "He could sit there all day. And when he does get hungry and go in, there's still your grandad."

"You'd think he'd know every word of that book by now," said Bell. "Does he do owt else but take exams?"

From *The Hollow Land* by Jane Gardam

Is Bell the **narrator** in this **extract**? How can you tell?

....

....

In which season of the year is this story **set**? How can you tell?

....

....

Are there any particularly **local words** in this **extract**? Are any of them the same as in the passage on page 24?

....

....

What type of writing do you think these **extracts** come from? Choose from these: ☐ D
historical adventure, fantasy, adventure, anecdote, biography, science fiction.

....

....

Now choose a landscape (town or country) that you know well, and write a **description** of it to form the **setting** for a story.

....

....

A questionnaire

Complete this brief **questionnaire** about your reading.

Fiction

Tick the types of **fiction** that you enjoy reading.

novels ☐   short stories ☐   science fiction ☐   historical ☐

adventure ☐   mystery ☐   fantasy ☐   others ....

My favourite **authors** are ....

My favourite **fiction** titles are ....

....

Poetry

Tick the types of **poems** that you enjoy.

ballads ☐   haiku ☐   cinquain ☐   free verse ☐

limericks ☐   shape poems ☐   others ....

My favourite **poets** are ....

My favourite **poems** are ....

....

Non-fiction

Tick the types of **non-fiction** that you enjoy reading.

sports ☐ games ☐ hobbies ☐   animal care ☐   computers ☐

science ☐ art ☐ music ☐   TV, film, etc. ☐   others ....

My favourite **non-fiction** titles are ....

....

Now write more about your favourite types of reading on a separate sheet of paper.
Try to persuade other people of your age to read the books or poems that you enjoy
the most. Take care with your **punctuation**, **spelling** and **handwriting**.

Prefixes

Read the following list of **prefixes,** then write the **prefixes** in **alphabetical order**.
Remember: A **prefix** is a group of letters added to the beginning of
a word to change its meaning.

post-   ante-   kilo-   pro-   geo-   bio-   retro-   vari-   zoo-   multi-

hydro-   sub-   extra-   ultra-   fore-   peri-   iso-   contra-   thermo-

....

....

Use a **dictionary** to find a word beginning with each of the **prefixes** listed above.
Write each word in a sentence that shows its meaning.   D

antechamber: We came to a small antechamber
before entering the main hall.

....

....

....

....

....

....

....

....

....

....

....

....

....

....

Suffixes

Follow the instructions below for each of the words in this list.

artist	importance	stationary	changeable	lioness
sorrowful	telegraph	clarify	advertise	magnetism
senseless	skilfully	happiness	headship	attitude
motion	cruelty	otherwise	pomposity	

1 Write the word in the first column of the **chart**.
2 Decide which part of the word is its **suffix**, and write it in the second column.
3 Think of another word with the same **suffix**, and check its spelling in a dictionary. $\boxed{D}$
4 Write the new word in the third column of the **chart**.
Remember: A **suffix** is a group of letters added to the end of a word to change its meaning.

artist	-ist	chemist

Joining sentences

The **sentences** below are about the game of chess, but they are in the wrong order. Read through the **sentences** and decide on the best order.

Computers play chess. Chess remains popular today. There are sixteen pieces on each side. Chess is a game for two people. "Checkmate" means that the king cannot move without being taken by another piece. The board and the pieces can be in any two contrasting colours. Pieces move in different ways. Computers sometimes beat human champions. Chess is played on a chequered board. It seems complicated at first. Each side has one king, one queen, two knights, two bishops, two rooks and eight pawns. The board is usually black and white. The game ends when one of the kings is "checkmated". Experts improve their game by learning special patterns of moves. Chess is a very old game.

Write the sentences in order here.

1 ....

2 ....

3 ....

4 ....

5 ....

6 ....

7 ....

8 ....

9 ....

10 ....

11 ....

12 ....

13 ....

14 ....

15 ....

All these **sentences** about chess are very short. **Join** some of the **sentences** to make the piece of writing read more fluently. You may need to add, remove or change some words, but make sure you keep all the main ideas. Write out your **sentences** on a separate sheet of paper.

Active and passive

Active sentences describe an action done **by the subject**.
I directed the award-winning film. (an **active** sentence)
Passive sentences describe an action done **to the subject**.
The award-winning film was directed by me. (a **passive** sentence)

Change these sentences from **passive** to **active**.

The match was won by our team.

Our team

The winning goal was scored by Rachel.

The party was enjoyed by all my friends.

Jack was stung by an unusual insect.

Now change these sentences from **active** to **passive**.

Aliens invade our planet.

Our planet is

Leonardo da Vinci painted the *Mona Lisa*.

The team dislike the group leader.

The hero piloted his craft with great skill.

A hurricane struck the town.

Colons, semicolons and dashes

Punctuation can be used to connect groups of words. The **punctuation marks** that do this are: the **colon (:)**, the **semicolon (;)** and the **dash (–)**.

Read each sentence below, and write another sentence using the same **punctuation marks**. **Remember**:

- A **colon** is used to introduce a list, a quotation or a second clause that makes the first clause easier to understand. (A clause is a group of words with a verb in it.)
- A **semicolon** is used to link complete clauses that are too closely related to separate with a full stop.
  It can also be used to separate items in a list that already has commas in it.
- A **dash** can be used to separate a comment from the rest of a sentence. It makes a stronger break than a comma and is less formal than brackets.

Bring these things with you: a jumper, your swimsuit, your lunch and your bus fare.

....

....

It was Shakespeare's Juliet who asked: "What's in a name?"

....

The match was abandoned: rain poured down.

....

....

We had to stop playing; I went to Matt's house.

....

I bought a kilo of big, juicy apples; two large, ripe lemons; a grapefruit and a punnet of delicious, sweet-smelling strawberries.

....

....

....

The weather is lovely – wish you were here!

....

Connectives

Here are some one-word **connectives**.

and	but	when	because
so	for	as	though

Choose a different one of these **connectives** to link each of the paired sentences below. **Remember: Connectives** are words or phrases that link together different parts of a text. **Connectives** that link sentences, clauses or parts of phrases are called **conjunctions**.

I fell over. I hurt my knee. ....
....

The game ended. The referee blew his whistle. ....
....

She couldn't ride her bike. It had a puncture. ....
....

I couldn't spell that word. I fetched the dictionary. ....
....

We arrived on time. The train was delayed. ....
....

Here are some **words** and **phrases** that can also be used as **connectives**.

also	however	this means	for example	as this

Fit the **connectives** above into the spaces in these three paragraphs.

Many kinds of words can be used to connect ideas in a piece of writing. F__r e_ _ _ _ _ _ _, pronouns, adverbs, and conjunctions are all useful.

T__ _ _ _ _ _ _ _s that we can make our writing more varied and more interesting to read. A_ _o, the words we choose can help us to make our meaning clearer to our readers.

H_ _ _ _ _ _r, we should try not to use too many of these connectives in a short piece, __s _ _ _ _s can make our sentences long and confusing.